Printed and Published in Great Britain by D.C. Thomson & Co., Ltd, 185 Fleet Street, London, EC4A 2HS.

CONTACT DETAILS By post: The Beano, D.C. Thomson & Co., Ltd, 2 Albert Square Dundee DD1 9 QJ
email: beano@dcthomson.co.uk phone: 01382 223131
PROMOTIONS promotions@dcthomson.co.uk
SYNDICATION syndication@dcthomson.co.uk
CIRCULATION circulation@dcthomson.co.uk
LICENSING start.licensing@btinternet.com

DENNIS - YOU'VE A LITTLE VISITOR!
CURLY! PIE FACE?
NO - IT'S WALTER!
GROAN! INSTANT RELAPSE!
SLUMP!
CHEER UP. I'VE BROUGHT YOU A PRESENT.
YOUR HOMEWORK - SO YOU DON'T FALL BEHIND AT SCHOOL.
HOMEWORK BOOK
DENNIS
DOUBLE RELAPSE!
TEACHER SAID YOU WERE IN BED WITH A BUG. WHAT KIND OF BUG?
NOSEY!

ARGH! IT'S HORRIBLE!
HELP! UGLY BUG!
BLITHERING TERROR!
ZOOM!
BRILLIANT ACTING GNASHER. THAT'S MADE ME FEEL BETTER!
DENNIS
NOW WHAT PESKY HOMEWORK DID THAT DRIP WALTER BRING ME?
HOMEWORK BOOK
DENNIS
WOW! I DON'T BELIEVE IT!

MY HOMEWORK IS TO WRITE MY OWN FILM - BEST HOMEWORK EVER!
Write an idea for your own film script.
I NEED A TITLE. 'DENNIS AND THE SEARCH FOR THE GOLDEN GNASHER'.
IDEA!
DENNIS JONES, THE BOLD EXPLORER LOOKED OUT ACROSS THE ENDLESS JUNGLE.
SCRIBBLE!
DENNIS WAS SEARCHING FOR A SOLID GOLD STATUE OF AN ABYSSINIAN TRIPE HOUND.
Lost Temple
BUT A DEEP DEEP RAVINE LAY IN HIS WAY.

BUT DENNIS HAD A BUNGEE ROPE IN HIS KIT BAG.
HE TOOK THE PLUNGE.
DIVE!
POYOINGG!
AND HIS ROPE SPRUNG HIM BACK UPWARDS.
TWAANG!
AND HE LANDED SAFELY ON THE OTHER SIDE.
THUD!
DENNIS HEARD SOMETHING BEHIND HIM.
WHAT NEW PERIL WAS THIS?
JAB!

NO BUNGEEING IN THE DEEP RAVINE.
WARDEN
RULE BOOK
GROAN. JUNGLE WALTER.
SNATCH! CHUCK!
MY LOVELY RULE BOOK.
RULE BOOK
MUST BREAK THE RULES AND SAVE MY BOOK.
DENNIS BRAVED THE DANGERS OF THE SWAMP.
UNTIL HE REACHED THE GREAT TEMPLE.

UP THE STAIRS HE BOUND.
OPENING THE GREAT TEMPLE DOORS.
SHOVE!
CREE-EAK!
AND HE STEPPED UP TO THE GOLDEN STATUE.
GNASHER
AA-AAA- CHOOO!!
WHAT'S THAT SMELL - POLLEN? I'M ALLERGIC!
DENNIS HAD RELEASED GNASHER FROM HIS SPELL. ENCASED IN POLLEN.
BOUND!
GNASHER

THAT'S NOT HOW WE REALLY MET. THE END.
SCRIBBLE!
I'M HANDING IN DENNIS'S HOMEWORK. BET IT'S HOPELESS.
SCHOOL
LATER AT SCHOOL -
AND THE WINNER IS . . .
ME!
NO, DENNIS!
NOO! MY PLAN BACKFIRED!
CLENCH!
CLENCH!
WON,
NO-O-O-O-O-O!
-TOM PATERSON-

Dennis and GNASHER
THIS BOOK BELONGS TO:
I'M ALL BETTER NOW - LIFT OFF!

PIE MAN
DRRRRINGG!
IT'S PIE DAY!
LEAP!
BOING!
AND IT'S TIME FOR PIE MAN TO GO ON PATROL!
A MASK SO NO-ONE WILL RECOGNISE THE REAL ME.
TIE!
THE PIE MOBILE AWAITS!
PIEMOBILE

VAVOOM!
ALL SEEMS QUIET!
SECRET LABORATORY
UNTIL NOW!
CRAASH!
CRUMP!
THE EXPERIMENTAL ROBOT HAS BLOWN A FUSE - PLEASE HELP!
IT'S A JOB FOR PIEMAN!
BEEP! BEEP!
PIEMOBILE
CLANK!
NOTHING CAN STOP THE RAMPAGING ROBOT!
FZZT!
FLAIL!
CRAZY ROBOT! RUN!
SWING!
BEEP!
STOMP!
TAKE ONE CUSTARD PIE!

SPLOT!
AND COVER THE ROBOT'S VISOR SO IT CAN'T SEE!
CHUCK!
HE'S TAME, NOW. THANKS, PIEMAN.
UNLESS A PIE STRIKES THE STRIKER!
HURL!
SPLAT!
DUFF!
THERE'S ONLY ONE PIE MAN!
CHEER!
CHANT!
THANKS, DISTANT FANS!
BEANOTOWN UNITED
ZOOM!
LEAP!
WHERE ELSE WOULD IT ESCAPE FROM? THE ICE RINK?
SCREEECH!

HERE TIGER. HAVE SOME NICE PIES.
LOB!
SLURP! DROOL!
AND SOME MORE.
CHUCK!
GUZZLE! GOBBLE! SCOFF!
THE TIGER'S TOO TIRED TO MOVE. LET'S RECAPTURE HIM.
BURP! BELCH!
SNORE!
A JOB WELL DONE BY PIE MAN. HOME I GO.
VROOM!
HOPE MUM HASN'T MISSED ME, OR GUESSED I'M REALLY PIE MAN.
TOM PATERSON
PIE FACE. COME AND WATCH THE NEWS. PIE MAN HAS BEEN SAVING THE TOWN. DON'T YOU WISH YOU WERE LIKE HIM?
PIE MAN TO THE RESCUE!
NOT A WORD, READERS.

DENNIS IN
WEIGH TO GO!
WAHOO! THE DAY BEGINS!
LEAP!
BOING!
I WONDER HOW I DID?
HOW WHO DID?
IT'S MUM. WHAT'S SHE DOING?
I DID IT! I LOST A WHOLE TWO POUNDS . . .
SKIP!
SPROING!

CAREFULLY WEIGH MY BREAKFAST. MUSTN'T OVERDO IT.
Weeto Chomps
DAD
WHY DO ADULTS WEIGH BORING THINGS INSTEAD OF INTERESTING THINGS?
LIKE FINDING OUT THE WEIGHT OF OUR HOUSE - THAT'S INTERESTING.
MUM WON'T NEED HER SCALES TODAY!
NOW TO LEVER UP THE HOUSE SO I CAN GET THE SCALES UNDER.

STOP THAT AT ONCE, DENNIS. YOU'RE DOING IT ALL WRONG.
RULE BOOK
FIRST, YOU TAKE A BRICK.
FIND OUT WHAT THE BRICK WEIGHS . . .
THEN YOU COUNT ALL THE BRICKS IN THE HOUSE.
ONE THOUSAND FOUR HUNDRED AND THIRTY THREE . . .
WEIGHING HEAVY THINGS, EH? I WEIGHED AN ELEPHANT, ONCE.

CHUG! CHUG!
ALL YOU NEED IS A BIG ENOUGH CRANE.
RUMBLE!
CLANK!
CREAK!
I'LL SOON HAVE THAT HOUSE OF YOURS WEIGHED.
NO, NO! USE THE MEGA BALLOONS FROM MY TRICK SHOP.
INFLATE THEM WITH HELIUM.
HISSS!
HELIUM

IS SOMEONE TRYING TO STEAL OUR HOUSE?
FLOAT!
HELP! THE BALLOONS ARE FLOATING ME AWAY!

COLONEL YOU'RE ARRESTED FOR ATTEMPTED HOUSE LIFTING.
SHAME!
NINE THOUSAND AND ELEV . . . BAH! LOST MY COUNT!
ENOUGH! EVERYONE OUT OF MY GARDEN. HOW DID ALL THIS GET STARTED?
RANT! RAVE!
THAT WAS GREAT FUN, GNASHER, BUT WE'D BETTER SNEAK A-'WAY'!
-TOM PATERSON-

WALTER IN
SPY IN THE SKY!
GNASH!
LEAP!

AND GOT TO DO.
BUILDING, EH? I'LL BET THEY DON'T HAVE BUILDING PERMISSION!
INTO THE TREEHOUSE PALS - DON'T WANT ANYONE TO LEARN OUR SECRET.
NAILS
PEER!
I HATE SECRETS WHEN I DON'T KNOW THEM - TIME TO GET SPYING.
SPYING FOR DUMMIES
THE BOOK SAYS A TRAMPOLINE CAN HELP YOU REACH PLACES TO SPY ON.
DRAG!

HERE GOES - BIG BOUNCE.
LEAP!
BOING!
NEARLY THERE!
BOUNCE!
BOING!
ARGH! MY SOFT HEAD!
KLUNK!
I'LL TRY A DIFFERENT APPROACH - A STETHOSCOPE IS A USEFUL LISTENING DEVICE.
LUMP LOTION
FIRST AID
I'LL PUT IT ON THE BARK OF THE MENACE TREE . . .
. . . AND HEAR WHAT THOSE MENACES ARE UP TO.
MUMBLE! MUTTER!

SWOOP!
DRRRRR!
RATATAT!
NOW FOR A GOOD OLD PECK!
RAT-TAT-TAT!!!
AARGH! I'M DEAFENED!
MASTER SPY WALTER WON'T BE BEATEN.
SOON -
LIKE MY CAT DISGUISE, READERS.
TIPPY-TOE

I'LL JUST CLIMB THE TREE - I'M AS AGILE AS A CAT!
ARGH! NO! GNASHER! I'M NOT A CAT - IT'S ME, WALTER!
GNASH! GNASH!
LEAP!
I'M STUCK - WHAT A SORRY TALE!
GNASH!
NEE-NAW! NER-NER!
CAT STUCK UP A TREE LADS - WE'VE GOT TO RESCUE IT! PITIFUL NOISES IT'S MAKING!
DOWN YOU COME, CAT BOY!
WHIMPER!
WHIRR!
CREAK!

NOW THEN YOUNG WALTER - IMPERSONATING A CAT IS A VERY SERIOUS OFFENCE.
SHAME!
WHAT'S BEEN GOING ON HERE? HAVE WE BEEN TOO BUSY WORKING TO SEE THE FUN?
NER NER!
SCREECH!
NOT TO WORRY, GNASHER'S HERE - WE'VE SOMETHING FOR YOU!
CLAP!
SLAP!
GNASH! GNASH!
HAPPY BIRTHDAY, BOY! THIS IS THE SECRET KENNEL WE WERE WORKING ON FOR YOU!
GNASHER
WAG! WAG!
PITY THAT NOSEY WALTER ISN'T HERE TO SEE IT!
-TOM PATERSON-

Dennis and Gnasher®
in 'PIG TALE'
I'M GOING TO PARIS FOR THE DAY.
TOUGH BEING A ROCK STAR'S DAUGHTER, ATHENA.
SOB! I'VE NO-ONE TO LOOK AFTER MY PETS!
DAB! DAB!
I'LL LOOK AFTER THEM. NOT CATS ARE THEY?
SHAKE!
NO, NOTHING AS COMMON AS CATS . . .
SNIFF!

BABY PIGS?
MICRO PIGS. THESE LITTLE GUYS ARE FULLY GROWN!
OINK!
LEAP!
SQUEAL!
OINKLE!
TRUST ATHENA TO HAVE FANCY PETS. HOW CAN I SMUGGLE THESE PAST MUM?
OINK!
SNORK
GRUNT!

YOUR SHOES ARE SQUEAKING, DENNIS!
SQUEAK!
SQUEAK!
WRIGGLE!

GOT AWAY WITH IT. ON YOU GO, PIGS.
PYOING!
OINK!

THEY'RE MENACE MICRO PIGS!
BOING!
BOING!

OI! COME BACK!
OINK!
SQUOINK
SCURRY!
ZOOM!

SKID!
THE PIGS! WHERE DID THEY GO?
TIME TO DUST MY DUCK ORNAMENTS . . .
DUST!
. . . AND MY THREE LITTLE PIGS!

WAIT A MINUTE. I DON'T HAVE THREE LITTLE PIGS!

CHOO!
IT SNEEZED!
SWOON!

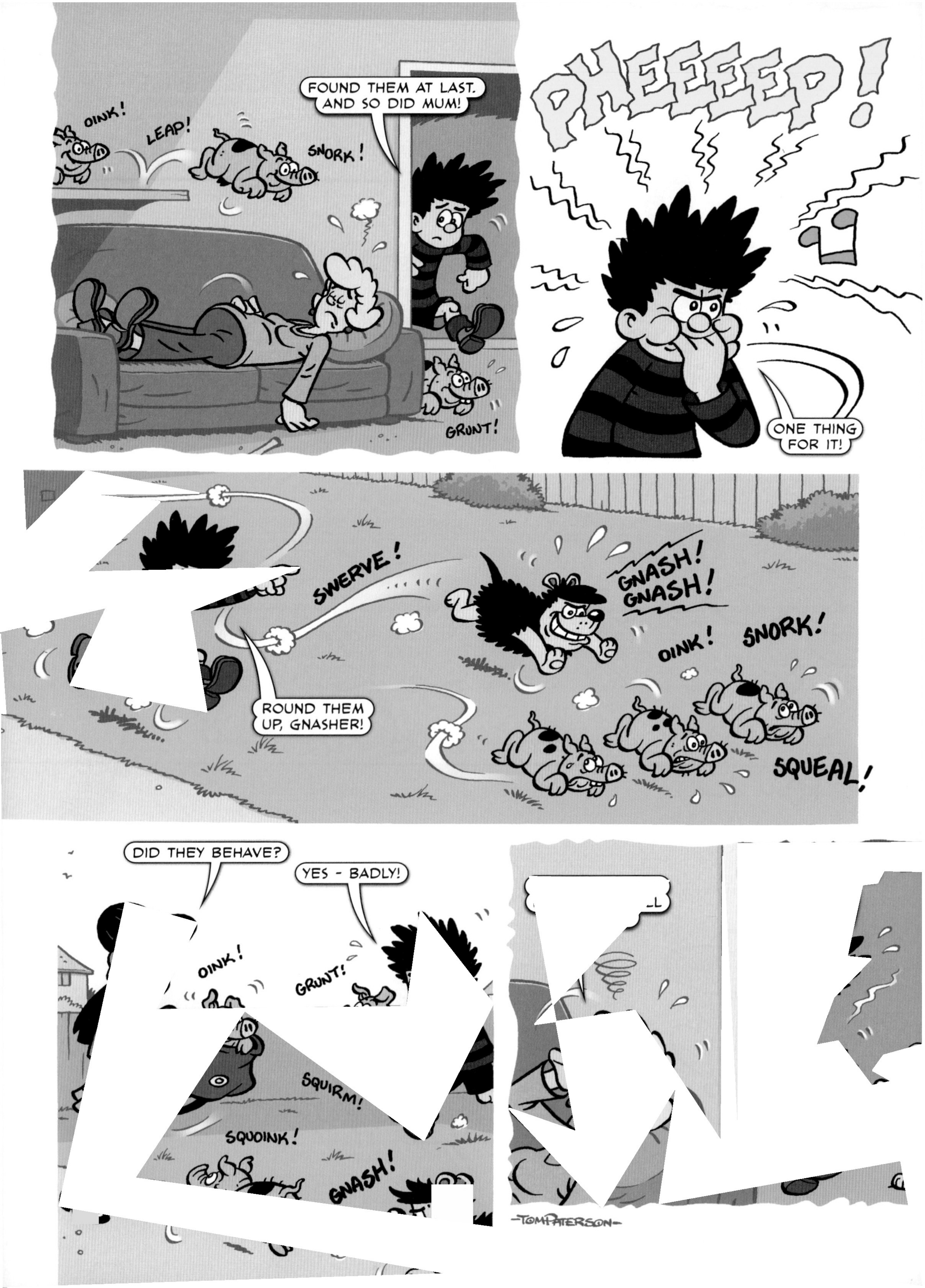
OINK!
LEAP!
SNORK!
FOUND THEM AT LAST. AND SO DID MUM!
GRUNT!
PHEEEEP!
ONE THING FOR IT!
SWERVE!
GNASH! GNASH!
ROUND THEM UP, GNASHER!
OINK!
SNORK!
SQUEAL!
DID THEY BEHAVE?
YES - BADLY!
OINK!
GRUNT!
SQUIRM!
SQUOINK!
GNASH!
-TOM PATERSON-

IT'S A DOG'S LIFE
TIME FOR SCHOOL! EVERYBODY INTO CLASS - EXCEPT FOR THE DOG. IT'S A SCHOOL RULE NO DOGS IN CLASS.
AW, BUT GNASHER IS MY BEST PAL!
POOR GNASHER. WHAT WILL HE DO ALL DAY?
BEANOTOWN SCHOOL
TRUDGE!
MOPE!
GNASH.
TROT!
PARK
KEEP OFF THE GRASS!
GNASH-GNASH!
WHAT'S THAT DOG DOING? HE WOULDN'T DARE.
KEEP OFF THE GRASS!

STEAM!
HE BLOOMIN' DID!
KEEP OFF THE GRASS!
TODDLE!
YOU PESKY MUTT!
SNAP!
GNASH-GNASH!
COME BACK HERE!
SLIDE!
WHEE!
ZOO OOM!
GNASH!
FLOP!

TWIRL!
WHIZZ!
GNASH?
ZWOOOP!
GNAAAAAASH!
SPIN!
WHIRL!
GNASH!
THERE YOU ARE, HOUND!
PHOOM!
FLYING DOG! DUUUCK!

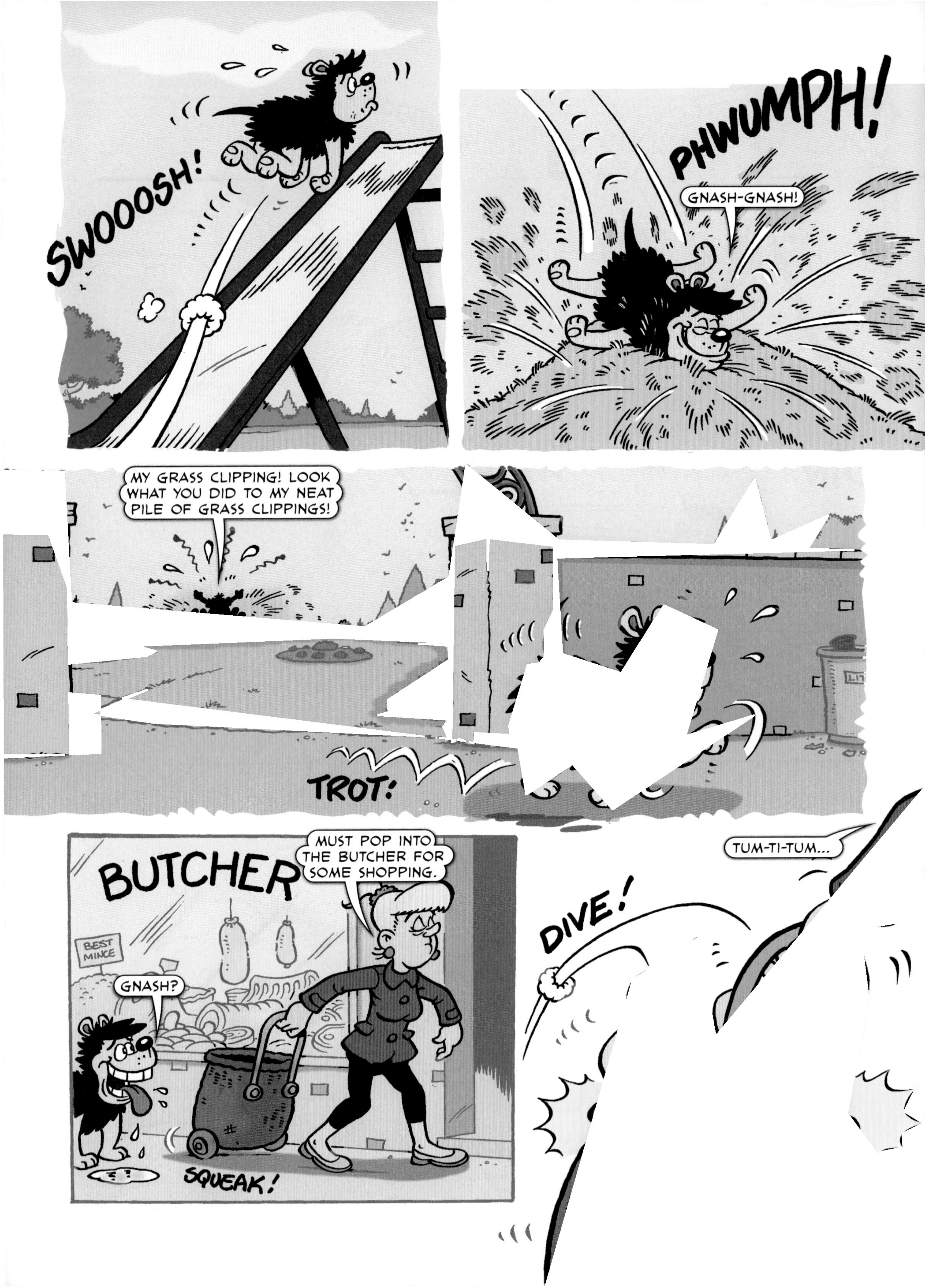
SWOOOSH!
PHWUMPH!
GNASH-GNASH!
MY GRASS CLIPPING! LOOK WHAT YOU DID TO MY NEAT PILE OF GRASS CLIPPINGS!
TROT!
BUTCHER
MUST POP INTO THE BUTCHER FOR SOME SHOPPING.
BEST MINCE
GNASH?
SQUEAK!
TUM-TI-TUM...
DIVE!

WHAT WOULD YOU LIKE TODAY? NICE SAUSAGES?
OOH, I DON'T REALLY KNOW... WHAT ELSE DO YOU HAVE?
GNASH.
GNASH! GNASH! GOBBLE! GUZZLE! CHOMP!
GONE!
GONE!
ER... I'VE GOT... NOTHING...
?
ALL GONE!

!?!
WE'VE BEEN BUSIER THAN I THOUGHT.
BURRP!

AM I HEARING THINGS OR DID YOUR SHOPPING BASKET JUST BURP?
OOOH.

THAT BLOOMIN' DOG!
BELCH!
CHOMP.
GNASH!
LEAP!
I HATE THAT DOG!
VWUMM!
COME BACK! I'LL GET YOU!
GNASH-GNASH
GALLOP!
BOUND!
PYOING!
DRAT. THE DOG GOT AWAY - THERE'S JUST THAT UGLY HAIRY BABY.
NO WONDER HE'S A BUTCHER - HE'S AS THICK AS MINCE!
BOUNCE!

BACK TO THE SHOP FOR ME.
FUME!
GNASH-GNASH-GNASH!
GNASH!
JAUNTY STRUT!
DRRRRINGG!
SCHOOL'S OUT TILL TOMORROW!
BEANOTOWN SCHOOL
GNASH... ZZZ...
HAVE YOU JUST BEEN LYING THERE SLEEPING ALL DAY YOU LAZY DOG?
I DON'T KNOW HOW YOU CAN JUST DO NOTHING ALL DAY.
GNASH-GNASH-GNASH!
WINK!
TOM PATERSON

DENNIS'S GREATEST INVENTIONS
NO 1.
THE TOTAL
GOALKEEPER KIT.
SPROING!
STRE-E-ETCH!
BOOMF!
PYOING!

DENNIS'S GREATEST INVENTIONS
WHEEE!
WHOP!
SPLOT! SPLAT!
SPLOFF! SPLAFF!
SWIPE!
SCOOP!
SPTOOM! SPTOOM!
DIG! DIG!
NO 2.
THE LAZY MENACE'S SNOWBALL MACHINE.

DENNIS'S GREATEST INVENTIONS
SHAKE! SHAKE!
FIZZ!
SWOOOOSH!
NO 3. GNASHER'S JET PROPELLED SKATEBOARD.
ZWOOM!

DENNIS'S GREATEST INVENTIONS
LEAP!
NO 4.
THE TREEHOUSE EMERGENCY ESCAPE CHUTE.

THE TALENTED TODDLER
BeA
GOO! GOO! TOY BRICKS!
CRAWL!
EMPTY 'EM ALL OUT! YEAH!
TIP!
CLATTER!

ME'S TRYIN' TO SPELL.
GOOGOO
GAGAA
5
BUT, ON THE OTHER SIDE OF THE BRICKS -
BEA'S A GENIUS! SHE'S DONE A VERY HARD SUM.
20X100
=2000
÷Q
IT'S OFF TO THE SCHOOL FOR TALENTED TODDLERS FOR YOU.
VOOM!
SCHOOL FOR TALENTED TODDLERS - MAYBE WALTER HAS HEARD OF IT!
PHOOOM!
SMARMY SMARTY-PANTS!
HEARD OF IT! I WAS FIRST IN CLASS!
YUCK!
1ST
POTTY

OH, NO. WHAT IF THEY TURN BEA INTO ANOTHER WALTER?
HORROR!
ADVANCED SWOTTERY
STRING THEORY
QUANTUM PHYSICS
SO, AT THE TALENTED TODDLER SCHOOL -
TALENTED TODDLER SCHOOL
PRIDE!
AH - WHAT A CLASS OF CLEVER CLOGS - LITTLE CLOGS.
MRS TEACHER! I'VE A LITTLE GENIUS TO JOIN YOUR CLASS!
SHE'LL HAVE TO PASS THE TESTS.
LET'S FIND OUT IF LITTLE BEA IS MUSICAL.

ERK! THAT'S NOT THE KIND OF MUSIC I'M USED TO!
PAARPLE-SQUEEKLE-ROOTY-TOOT!
PHOOT!
POOP-POOP TWEETLE PHREEP!
PASS THE OXYGEN!
GAG!
UMM!
HALF-GASSED GIBBER!
I'M SURE SHE'LL FIT RIGHT IN WITH THE OTHER GENIUSES. I'LL COLLECT HER LATER.
CHUFFED!
EGGY STENCH!
SKIP!
WE'VE GOT TO GET HER OUT OF THERE, GNASHER.
DO YOU WANT TO JOIN US IN OUR HARD SUMS LESSON, BEA?
EXTRA HARD SUMS
ONE QUICK ESCAPE PLAN!
SCRIBBLE!

MAKE A PAPER DART OF IT!
FOLD!
AND FLY IT, MENACE AIRLINES, TO BEA.
CHUCK!
ME CAN DO THIS!
SEE-SAW - BIG BOOK . . .
HURL!
ADVANCED ALGEBRA
WHEEE!
PYOING!
ME FREE!
I'VE GOT YOU!
COME BACK, YOU MENACES!
BEA'S VERY TALENTED - AT BEING A MINI MENACE.

THE COLONEL IN
FLOWER POWER!
THE COLONEL'S PLAYING WITH HIS REMOTE CONTROL TOYS.
OOPS. MY TANK'S WANDERED OFF INTO DENNIS'S GARDEN.
CRUNCH!
CLANK!
OH DEAR. THE SILLY TANK'S KNOCKED OVER DENNIS'S MUM'S FLOWER POT.
WHIRR!
I'LL REPLACE IT, BUT AN ACTION HERO LIKE ME CAN'T BE SEEN IN A FLOWER SHOP.
FIRST, ON WITH THE CAMOUFLAGE.
SMUDGE! DAB!
THEN I'LL TAKE TO MY UNDERGROUND TUNNELS.
CREAK!

IT'S THIS WAY, SOMEWHERE!
CAN'T FIND THE STEPS TO THE FLOWER SHOP. I'LL JUST GO UP THIS LADDER.
FLOWER SHOP STRAIGHT UP.
FEEDY TIME, PLANTS. DON'T RUSH! HEE! HEE! JUST MY LITTLE JOKE.
!?!
HELP! MY PLANT DID MOVE!
EEK! A PAIR OF HORRIBLE EYES.
CREAK!
AND A HORRIBLE GREEN FACE.

LET'S SEE. IN CASE OF PANIC - WATER MAY CALM SOMEONE DOWN.
RULE BOOK
EEK! HELP! MAD COLONEL!
THIS SHOULD BE ENOUGH!
GRAB!
WATER
THIS'LL MAKE YOU CALM!
HURL!
SWOOSH!
DUCK!
SLOOSH!
OI! WHO'S THROWING WATER AT ME? I'LL BASH THEM!

SOON -
SETTLE DOWN, EVERYONE. I'M SURE THERE'S A REASONABLE EXPLANATION.
MUCH ARGUING LATER -
THINK I GOT AWAY WITHOUT CAUSING TOO MUCH FUSS.
NOW TO REPLACE THE BROKEN FLOWER. NO-ONE WILL EVER KNOW.
ENTER DENNIS -
BOOT!
RESULT! I WAS SURE I'D BROKEN MUM'S FLOWER PLAYING FOOTBALL TODAY!
DENNIS! AFTER ALL THAT - IT WASN'T MY TANK'S FAULT!
-TOM PATERSON-

GNASHER IN...
LARK IN THE PARK!
IT'S YOUR FAVOURITE GAME, GNASHER. OFF TO THE PARK TO PLAY WITH YOUR FLYING RING.
PARK
GNASH!
READY, GNASHER? HERE GOES!
HURL!
ZINGGG!
FETCH, BOY!

KLAANG!
LEAP!
2
WHAT A GOALKEEPER YOU'D MAKE, GNASHER.
TROT!
RIGHT. COMING UP, ONE MENACE POWERED THROW.
GNYIP! WATER - DON'T NEED A BATH.
WHEEEE!
SCREECH!
AW, GNASHER. THAT'S YOUR FAVOURITE TOY!
PARK
SPALOYP!

YOU'LL HAVE TO BRAVE THE WATER IF YOU WANT IT BACK, BOY.
GOOD DOG, GNASHER. FIND THAT RING.
DIVE!
NO, GNASHER. THAT OLD TOILET SEAT IS NOT YOUR TOY!
GNASHER GOES UNDER AGAIN -
PLUNGE!
SPLOOSH!
SHAKE!
WRONG AGAIN, BOY. THAT'S AN OLD BICYCLE WHEEL - MAYBE EVEN ONE OF MINE.
THIRD TIME LUCKY!
BLOYPLE! BLOOP!

GOOD DOG, GNASHER. KNEW YOU COULD DO IT!
ON SECOND THOUGHTS, IT'S NOT WHAT IT LOOKED. THAT'S THE PLUG FOR THE POND.
PROUD!
PLUG
SO WHAT'S KEEPING ALL OF THE WATER IN?
BLURPLE! BLOIP!
GURGLE! SWIRL!
NOTHING. NOW WE HAVE ONE EMPTY POND!
FLAP! GAASP!

BETTER FILL IT UP AGAIN BEFORE ANYBODY NOTICES.
COME ON CURLY AND PIE FACE - LET'S GET THE POND RE-FILLED!
SINCE IT'S ALL GNASHER'S FAULT, WHY DOESN'T HE HELP?
TIP!
GOOD POINT, CURLY.
CHUCK!
SLOSH!
OI, GNASHER. WHAT ARE YOU GOING TO DO TO HELP?
STUPID QUESTION, REALLY. WON'T BE SWIMMING IN THERE FOR A WHILE.

YOU'RE HAVING A LAUGH!

NO? TRY THIS ONE, THEN.
STILL DEEP GLOOM. THIS IS SERIOUS.
MUST FIND HIS LAFF-O-METER.
WALTER! DINNER'S READY!
HAR. WALTER SHOULDN'T HAVE LEFT IT WITHIN MY REACH.

NOW FOR A FEW ADJUSTMENTS TO THIS.
FIDDLE! TWIDDLE!
JUST IN TIME. WALTER'S COMING BACK.
HEY, WALTER. DENNIS HAS GONE TO THE JOKE SHOP TO MAKE MR HAR HAR LAUGH.
NOT WHILE I HAVE MY LAFF-O-METER!
HE FELL FOR IT!
RIGHT, YOU TWO. ANY LAUGHING AND MY MACHINE WILL KNOW.
OPEN
FALSE BOTTOMS

WATCH THIS
ARGH! PEPPER
ACHOO! GET IT OFF!
PHUFF!
SWOOSH!
GLUB! WATER -
COLD WATER!
TRAITOR. THE
LAFF-O-METER
TURNED AGAINST ME!
CHUCK!
HAR! HAR! HAR!
HAR! HAR! HAR!
BANG!
THUMP!

PIE-FACE IS LOST IN THE PIE JUNGLE. HOW MANY PIES CAN YOU COUNT ON THIS PAGE?
ANSWER - 47

DENNIS IS ADMIRING THE MENACE SHEEP WHICH PROVIDE WOOL FOR HIS JERSEYS. HOW MANY SHEEP CAN YOU SPOT ON THIS PAGE?
CUD COLA
ANSWER - 20

GNASHER'S ON A TOUR OF THE SAUSAGE FACTORY. HOW MANY SAUSAGES ARE IN THIS PICTURE?
OFF
AUTOMATIC SAUSAGE MAKER
ON
ANSWER - 62

RATBUCKET'S NEW GUITAR!
HEY, DENNIS! I'VE GOT A JOB FOR YOU!
IT'S RATBUCKET . . . ATHENA'S ROCK STAR DAD!
NO WAY - I'M NOT WASHING YOUR FANCY CAR FOR YOU.
NO - THERE'S A NEW GUITAR I'D LIKE YOU TO PICK UP FOR ME AT THE MUSIC SHOP. I'LL PAY YOU! BUT DON'T EVEN LOOK AT IT!
BANK OF DOSHLAND
KACHING!

I'M HERE TO COLLECT A GUITAR FOR MR RATBUCKET!
MUSIC SHACK
99
SCREECH!
ZOOM!
GRUNGE
WOW! WONDER WHAT IT LOOKS LIKE? ONE SMALL PEEK WON'T HURT!
WOW! WHAT A BEAUTY!
I'VE NO IDEA WHERE DENNIS IS, CURLY. WE'VE BEEN LOOKING ALL MORNING.
PIEMOBILE
PHOOM!
IF WE KEEP DRIVING ROUND WE'LL MAYBE BUMP INTO HIM SOON.
VROOM!

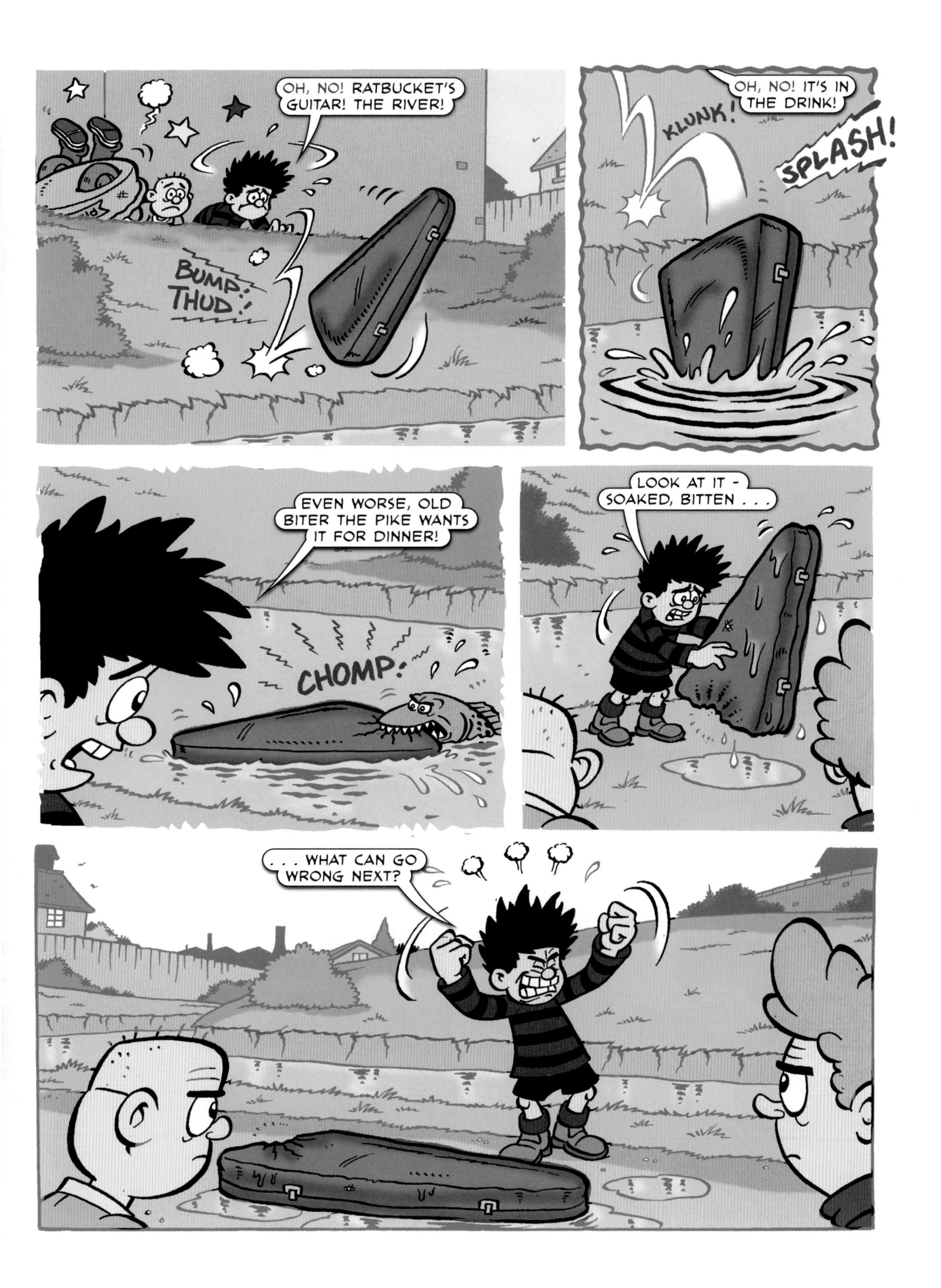
OH, NO! RATBUCKET'S GUITAR! THE RIVER!
BUMP! THUD!
OH, NO! IT'S IN THE DRINK!
KLUNK!
SPLASH!
EVEN WORSE, OLD BITER THE PIKE WANTS IT FOR DINNER!
CHOMP!
LOOK AT IT - SOAKED, BITTEN . . .
. . . WHAT CAN GO WRONG NEXT?

INI ROLLER CAN
WRONG, NEXT.
CHUGGA-CHUGG!
RUMBLE! MANGLE! KRUNCH!
JUST LOOK AT THE NEW GUITAR, NOW.
AH! DENNIS WITH A STRANGE SECRET WEAPON, I'LL PAINT BALL IT!
WHIRR!
GROAN. NOW A COLOUR CHANGE.
SPLOT! SPLAT! SPLUT!
PTOOM!
BETTER GET THIS TO RATBUCKET WHILE IT'S STILL IN ONE PIECE. OK, CURLY - PIE FACE?

S-SORRY, DENNIS. YOU'RE ON YOUR OWN. RATBUCKET'S SCARY.
ZOOM!
WHOOSH!
ER - MISTER, R. - HERE'S YOUR GUITAR. IT'S HAD A TEENY WEENY ACCIDENT.
AS I PLANNED.
AS, Y-YOU, P-PLANNED?
CRINGE!
SWEAT!
NERVOUS GIGGLE!
I KNEW YOU'D HAVE TO TAKE A LOOK AT IT, AND IT WOULD HAVE SOME ADVENTURES WITH YOU. DON'T LIKE NEW THINGS!
CAN I TRY IT OUT?
ROCK ON, DENNIS, NO-ONE ELSE HAS A GUITAR LIKE MINE!

DAD IN
DON'T PANIC!
MA-MA!
ON YOU GO!
AN' DOWN YOU GO!
SHOVE!
WHEEE!
RATTLE!
BONE PIE
SNORE! YIP! YELP!
CLATTER!
KLONK!
GNERK!

PHOOM!
I'VE BEEN ATTACKED!
JUST GOT MY NEW DELIVERY OF STINK BOMBS FROM MR HAR HAR'S SHOP.
STINK BOMBS
EXTRA EGGY
DENNIS! HELP!
BOOMPH!
LEAP!
STEADY, GNASHER! MY STINK BOMBS!
OH, OH. THEY'RE GOING TO LAND ON . . .

. . . DAD!
BEA?
TWITCH! SNIFF!
HARRASSED PARENT MONTHLY
NO - IT'S EVEN
GIBBER!
NOSTRIL-NUMBING NIFF!
THAT DOES IT! ONLY ONE THING FOR IT . . .
CHOKE! GAG! HEAVE!
. . . MAKE FOR MY PANIC ROOM.
GRAB!
PHEW! I'LL BE SAFE FROM ALL THOSE MENACES IN HERE.
SLAM!

I'M BACK FROM THE SHOPS - WHAT'S BEEN GOING ON IN HERE? AND WHERE'S DAD?
HE'S IN HIS PANIC ROOM, MUM!
OH, IS HE?
DAD! GET OUT HERE THIS INSTANT!
SPORT
YOU'RE SUPPOSED TO BE LOOKING AFTER THEM - NOT HIDING IN YOUR ROOM.
GROAN. WE'RE ALL ON CLEANING UP DUTIES!
SLOP!
WHILE I TAKE IT EASY IN DAD'S PANIC ROOM. AAAH!
DAD'S PANIC ROOM
MUSHY TALES of LOVE
CORRIE

MAKE IT SNAPPY!
TEAM PHOTO EVERYONE! SAY 'CHEESE'!
AND GET READY FOR A SOAKING.
RANCID CABBAGE WATER
-TOM PATERSON-

IT'S ALL GO WITH GRAN!
WE'RE GOING TO VISIT GRAN TODAY!
AND GNIPPER, OF COURSE!
GNASHER AND GNIPPER ARE ALWAYS HAPPY TO SEE EACH OTHER.
GNIP-GNIP!
GNASH-GNASH!
BUT GRAN DOESN'T LOOK SO HAPPY. WHAT'S THE MATTER, GRAN?
OH, NOTHING MUCH...
IT'S JUST THAT MY CHARLEY DAVIDSON MOTORBIKE HAS TO GO IN TO THE GARAGE FOR ITS MILLION-MILE CHECK-UP. THAT'S ITS THIRD THIS YEAR ALREADY.
GARAGE

SO I'M A BIT FED UP BECAUSE I DON'T HAVE ANY WHEELS TO GET AROUND ON.
HO-HUMM!
DON'T WORRY, GRAN. WE'LL GET YOU MOVING AGAIN.
SHUFFLE!
I HAVEN'T GOT A CLUE HOW WE'LL GET HER MOVING BUT I'LL THINK OF SOMETHING.
SO...
TRY SKATEBOARDING, GRAN.
I'M NOT SURE, DENNIS...
...MY BALANCE ISN'T WHAT IT WAS.
WOBBLE!
THIS ISN'T AS EASY AS IT LOOKS.
WOOOOPS! THANKS FOR CATCHING ME, DENNIS!
FLIP!
SQUOMF!
YEOW!

N-NO PROBLEM, GRAN. WE'LL TRY SOMETHING ELSE.
I'LL MAKE A NICE CUPPA.
AND I'LL SEE IF YOU HAVE ANYTHING USEFUL IN THE SHED.
THERE'S LOADS OF GREAT BROKEN STUFF IN HERE. THERE MUST BE SOMETHING I CAN USE.
SNIFF-SNIFF! SOMETHING SMELLS A BIT OFF. WAS THAT YOU, GNASHER?
GNOT ME!
PIGGY HUMMM!
HARLEY PIG.
IT'S HARLEY, GRAN'S PET PORKER - AND HE'S GIVEN ME AN IDEA.
HAMMER! BANG! THUD!
GNO IDEA WHAT DENNIS IS DOING.

FINISHED, DENNIS?
INDEED I AM, GRAN.
WELL, IT LOOKS LOVELY.
BUT WILL IT BE FAST ENOUGH FOR ME?
DON'T WORRY.
CLICK!
JUST LET ME FUEL UP YOUR ENGINE. TURNIPS, HARLEY?
LOB!
CHOMP-CHOMP! MUNCH-MUNCH!
GUZZLE! GOBBLE! CHOMF!
BRRP.

OH-OH! MY TUM'S GOING TO...
BLURBLE! SQUOYLCH! GURGLE! BLOYP!
HEE-HEE! HE'S FAST ENOUGH, DENNIS - HE'S JET POWERED!
PAARP!
PHWAART!
WAHEY! GRAN'S GOT A CHAIR-IOT!
PHOOM!
BRRRRAAAPP!

DOWNHILL ALL THE WAY!
THIS HILL LOOKS PERFECT, PALS - GET THE FLAGS.
DENNIS AND SNOW - A BAD COMBINATION. WONDER WHAT HE'S UP TO?
HMM. THEY SEEM BUSY ENOUGH.
ONE THERE - ANOTHER THERE . . .
WE'VE BEEN BUSY, OK - MAKING A DOWNHILL SLALOM RACE.
AND I'M GOING TO BE FIRST TO TRY IT OUT ON MY SNOWBOARD.
NOW TO SET THE TIME TO BEAT.

SWISH!
WAHEY! GET READY FOR A RECORD THAT WILL NEVER BE BEATEN.
ZOOM!
FLIP!
SWOOSH!

HAR! HAR! WALTER!
DON'T LAUGH - MUMMY AND DADDY TAKE ME SKI-ING EVERY YEAR. I'M EXCELLENT ON THE SLOPES.
PROVE IT!
QUICK - WHILE HE'S NOT LOOKING MOVE THE FLAGS FURTHER APART.
50 -
HMM. MY CALCULATIONS SEEM TO BE A LITTLE BIT OUT.
!
SWOOPH!
AND THE NEXT FLAG SEEMS MILES AWAY.
OH, DEAR. THOSE POOR WINTER FLOWERS!
WALTER HATES RULES BEING CHANGED.
VWOOF!
CRUSH!

I'M BACK ON TRACK AGAIN. NOW TO SPEED UP.
OI, WE'RE JUST FEEDING THE DUCKS!
SORRY - I DON'T THINK DENNIS CAME THIS WAY.
TO THE NEXT FLAG!
CRASH!
PARK KEEPER
OOPS! THE COURSE GOES THROUGH THE PARK KEEPER'S HUT!
PARKIE'S A BIT ANGRY - I'LL KEEP GOING.
!
SWOOPH!
?
THERE'S THE LAST FLAG, BUT IT SEEMS TO BE MOVING.

HAR! HAR! HERE'S WHY IT'S MOVING. GOOD DOG, GNASHER.
GALLOP!
YOU ROTTERS! I DIDN'T BEAT YOUR TIME.
YES - WE CHEATED A BIT . . .
. . . BUT ALTHOUGH YOU DIDN'T BREAK MY RECORD AT THE SLALOM . . .
. . . YOU BEAT ME FOR BREAKING ALL THE PARK RULES, WALTER.
?
-TOM PATERSON-
COME BACK, WALTER, YOU PEST!
OOH. I'VE NEVER BROKEN A PARK RULE IN MY LIFE - TILL NOW.
PARKY

AN APPLE FOR THE CREECHER!
DRRRING!
SMASH!
QUIET, YOU MENACE.
NOW FOR SOME RELAXING EASTERN EXERCISES.
RELAXING?
DENNIS! HIYAAH!
CHOP!
SWIPE!
LEAP!
KICK!

NOW FOR A PEACFUL BATH BEFORE I GO TO SCHOOL.
ARGH! I'M IMAGINING MY DUCK HAS A DENNIS HEAD!
SINK THAT DUCK!
I'M CALM AGAIN. I'LL JUST PAINT FACES ON MY HARD BOILED EGGS!
DENNIS FACES!
SPLOT! DAB!
TAKE THAT, EGGS!
CHOP!

RIGHT. I'M JUST ABOUT READY TO FACE ANOTHER DAY OF DENNIS.
STOMP!
NEARLY NINE O'CLOCK - WONDER WHAT HE'S UP TO?
THARRUMP! DARRUMP!

I WAS A BIT ROUGH ON MRS CREECHER. I'M GOING TO MAKE IT UP TO HER.

APPLE FOR THE TEACHER.
SHOVE!

LAST THING I EXPECTED!
SWOON! CRAASH!
!?!
SOME PEOPLE HAVE NO GRATITUDE.

HEDGE ROW!
YOU MAY TRIM THE HEDGE, WALTER. YOU ARE A VERY ARTISTIC BOY.
OOH, THANKS, DAD.
HMM. MY CHANCE TO MAKE A MASTERPIECE.

SNIP! SNIP!
CHECK OUT WALTER, GNASHER. WE CAN HAVE SOME FUN HERE.
CLIP! CLIP!
A WONDERFUL LIKENESS IF I DO SAY SO MYSELF.
LET'S GET TRIMMING, GNASHER.
ZOOM!
DAD'S HEDGE TRIMMERS ARE A BIT BLUNT . . .
. . . BUT I'LL HAVE A GO, ANYWAY.
SNIP! SNIP!
CLIP!

HAR! HAR! HOW D'YOU LIKE THAT SCULPTURE, WALTER?
WHAT A CHEEK!
I'M NOT TAKING THIS LYING DOWN.
SNIP!
GRR! HE'S TRIMMED A SERGEANT SLIPPER JUST TO ANNOY ME.
AND IT WORKED!

MY TURN, NOW!
SNIP! CLIP!
A GNASHER TO ANNOY WALTER!
CLIP!
I'LL HAVE REVENGE!
THERE! A CAT TO ANNOY GNASHER!
VERY SUCCESSFUL, WALTER!
WHIRRR!
GRR! CAT!

OO-ER! MY FENCE - GNASHED!
GNASH! CRUNCH!
MY LOVELY CAT SCULPTURE!
GNASH! RRRIPP! SHRED!
HAVE YOU TRIMMED THE HEDGE YET, WALTER?
ER - IS THAT TRIMMED ENOUGH, DAD?
MY ONCE LOVELY HEDGE.
POOR WALTER - HE'S BUSHED!
SHAME!
INSIDE!
-TOM PATERSON-